BINKY

UNDER PRESSURE

KIDS CAN PRESS

To Mom and Dad, for all their support and love

Text and illustrations © 2011 Ashley Spires

Kids Can Press acknowledges the financial support of the Government of Ontario, through the Ontario Media Development Corporation's Ontario Book Initiative; the Ontario Arts Council; the Canada Council for the Arts; and the Government of Canada, through the BPIDP, for our publishing activity.

Published in Canada by
Kids Can Press Ltd.
25 Dockside Drive
Toronto, ON M5A 0B5

Published in the U.S. by
Kids Can Press Ltd.
2250 Military Road
Tonawanda, NY 14150

www.kidscanpress.com

The artwork in this book was rendered in ink, watercolor, cat fur, bits of kitty litter and the occasional paw print.
The text is set in Fontoon.

Edited by Tara Walker
Series designer: Karen Powers
Designed by Rachel Di Salle and Marie Bartholomew

The hardcover edition of this book is smyth sewn casebound.
The paperback edition of this book is limp sewn with a drawn-on cover.
Manufactured in Shen Zhen, Guang Dong, P.R. China, in 4/2012 by Printplus Limited

CM 11 0 9 8 7 6 5 4 3 2
CM PA 11 0 9 8 7 6 5 4 3 2

Library and Archives Canada Cataloguing in Publication

Spires, Ashley, 1978–
        Binky under pressure / by Ashley Spires.

(A Binky adventure)
ISBN 978-1-55453-504-0 (bound). ISBN 978-1-55453-767-9 (pbk.)

I. Title. II. Series: Spires, Ashley, 1978– . Binky adventure.

PS8637.P57B555 2010   j741.5'971   C2011-901071-2

Kids Can Press is a *Corus*™ Entertainment company

BINKY

UNDER PRESSURE

by ASHLEY SPIRES

IT SHOULDN'T BE HERE.

THIS SPACE STATION IS KNOWN TO BE A DANGEROUS PLACE FOR ALIENS.

WHAP!

BUT SOMETIMES, ONE OF THEM JUST HAS TO TRY …

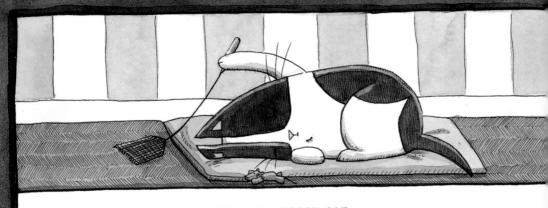

BINKY IS A SPACE CAT.

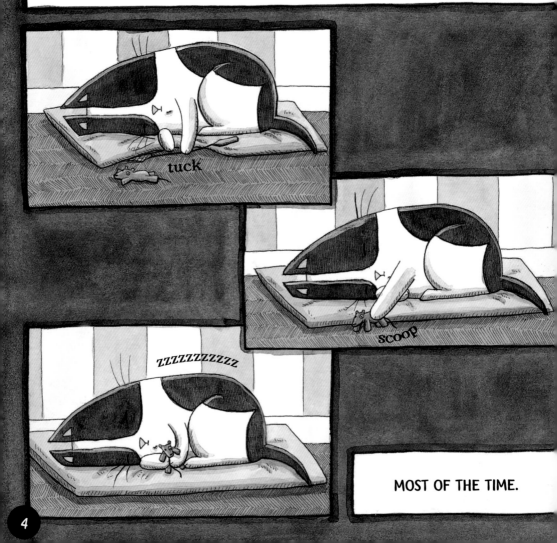

tuck

scoop

ZZZZZZZZZZZ

MOST OF THE TIME.

4

HE BUILT A ROCKET SHIP ...

rumble
rumble

BUT HE COULDN'T LEAVE HIS HUMANS.

HE WENT INTO **OUTER SPACE** ...

scritch

shimmy

buzzzzz

BUT IT WAS WAY
TOO MUCH WORK.

whoosh

swipe

BUT HIS LIFE HAS BECOME ROUTINE.

NAP.

ALIEN.

NAP.

EAT.

WASH.

NAP.

EAT.

NAP.

CUDDLE.

NAP.

NAP.

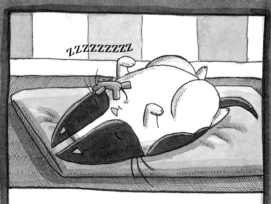

UNTIL ONE MORNING ...

BUT THAT'S **HIS** FOOD AND LITTER!

JUST WHO IN THE FUZZBUTT DOES SHE THINK SHE IS?!

MEORR??

Don't worry, Binky. There's plenty enough to share.

All you do is sleep anyway. Maybe you should cut down on the snacks and get some exercise.

poke

THIS IS ALL HAPPENING SO FAST.

BINKY NEEDS SOME TIME ALONE TO THINK.

WHY WOULD HIS HUMANS DO THIS TO HIM?

ANOTHER CAT? WASN'T HE ENOUGH FOR THEM?

HE WAS HERE FIRST.

THIS IS **HIS** SPACE STATION.

THOSE ARE **HIS** HUMANS!

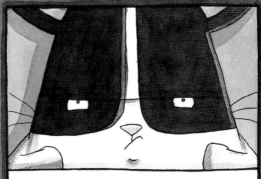

THAT IS **HIS** FOOD!

swoosh

AND THAT IS **HIS** BEST FRIEND!

ENOUGH IS ENOUGH.

HE'S NOT TAKING THIS LYING DOWN.

THAT'S BETTER.

CLEARLY, THIS SPACE STATION IS ONLY BIG ENOUGH FOR ONE KITTY.

BUT HOW CAN HE GET HER TO LEAVE?

OF COURSE!

HE'LL JUST ASK!

IF BINKY EXPLAINS THAT HE WAS HERE FIRST ...

THEN SHE IS SURE TO UNDERSTAND.

PROBLEM SOLVED.

SHE IS GOOD.

HE UNDERESTIMATED HER.

IN ORDER TO DEFEND HIS TURF ...

BINKY MUST LEARN MORE ABOUT THIS NEW INTRUDER.

HE CAN FIND A WAY TO GET HER OUT OF HIS SPACE STATION.

SO FAR, SHE APPEARS TO BE PERFECT.

A BIT **TOO** PERFECT ...

Flaws: 0
soft fur
perky ears
cute wiskers
lots of stripes

MAYBE SHE ISN'T A CAT AT ALL!

27

IF GRACIE LEAVES THE ALIEN ALONE ...

THEN BINKY WILL KNOW THAT SHE IS THE ENEMY.

SHE HAS **GOT** TO BE A ROBOT.

BUT SHE DEFEATED THE ALIEN ...

SO GRACIE AND BINKY MUST BE ON THE SAME SIDE!

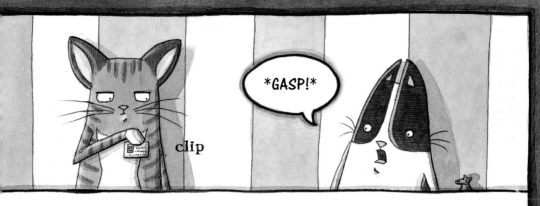

SHE'S NOT A ROBOT, SHE'S HIS **BOSS!**

A HIGH-RANKING F.U.R.S.T. OFFICIAL IS IN **HIS** SPACE STATION!

BUT WHY?

F.U.R.S.T. — Felines of the Universe Ready for Space Travel

Space Cat Annual Evaluation

All F.U.R.S.T. officers will undergo performance testing and be evaluated by a superior. A passing grade is necessary in order to maintain space cat status. Failure will result in immediate dismissal without treats.

Sincerely,

Sergeant Fluffy Vandermere

BINKY ISN'T WORRIED.

HHAA

HE IS CONFIDENT IN HIS SPACE CAT ABILITIES.

BUT CAPTAIN GRACIE ...

HAS SOME CONCERNS.

F.U.R.S.T. TOP-SECRET TECHNOLOGY LEFT IN ENEMY TERRITORY.

FAILURE TO REPORT AN ALIEN WARSHIP TO F.U.R.S.T. COMMAND.

pitta patta   pad pad

buzzshhh!

UNAUTHORIZED TUNNEL COMPROMISING SAFETY OF THE SPACE STATION.

shrug

PERHAPS THIS EXAM WON'T BE AS EASY AS HE THOUGHT.

SURE, BINKY HAS
MADE A FEW MISTAKES.

punch

kick

woosh

BUT SOON CAPTAIN GRACIE WILL SEE HIS INCREDIBLE SKILLS AND REFLEXES.

SPACE CAT OF THE YEAR

clap

clap

clap

HE'LL PROBABLY GET AN AWARD FOR HIS
OUTSTANDING PERFORMANCE.

ZZZ

ZZZZZ

ZZZZZZZ

CLANG! CLANG! BANG!

HOLY FUZZBUTT!!
WHAT THE ——— ?

MEOW-RA!

THE ALIENS HAVE INVADED
THE SPACE STATION!

MEE-MEOW!

MEW MEW!

THEY HAVE CAPTURED
HIS HUMANS AND ARE
COMING FOR **HIM!**

HE'S DOOMED!

dash

sproing!

scrape
scurza

trinkle

scritcha
scratch

WHERE IS CAPTAIN GRACIE? DID THE ALIENS GET HER?

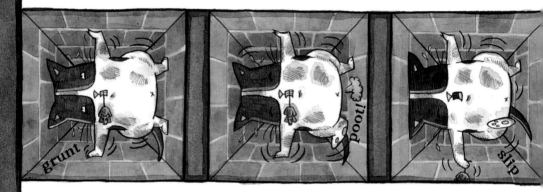

BINKY MUST STAY HIDDEN, BUT HE CAN'T HOLD ON MUCH LONGER ...

Binky! What on earth are you doing in there?

HIS HUMANS ARE SAFE!

launch

OH! You're filthy!

Why can't you stay out of trouble like Gracie?

GASP!

41

GRACIE!

OF COURSE!

THERE WAS NO INVASION.

IT WAS ONLY A TEST.

IF THIS IS WHAT GIRLS ARE LIKE, HE'S GLAD HE'S FIXED.

grrr!

spring

thud

slip

crash

oof!

foop!

BANG!

AFTER A MINOR SETBACK, BINKY TASTES VICTORY.

THAT'S ODD. HE DOESN'T REMEMBER ALIENS HAVING STRINGS ...

THESE TESTS AREN'T FAIR!

HE'S HAD NO TIME TO PREPARE!

THE SUN WAS IN HIS EYES ...

HE SKIPPED LUNCH ...

HE'S SUFFERING FROM SPACE GAS ...

AND HE HAS A HAIRBALL COMING ON.

HE'D LIKE TO SEE **HER** DO BETTER.

BINKY HAS BEEN TRICKED TWICE.

THIS IS SERIOUS.

IT'S TIME TO SHOW HER WHO'S BOSS.

NO MORE MR. NICE KITTY.

49

THE TESTS ARE OVER AT LAST.

IT'S THE MOMENT OF TRUTH.

DOES BINKY GET TO REMAIN A SPACE CAT? DID HE PASS?

THIS IS NOT A TEST. **THE SPACE STATION IS UNDER ATTACK!**

BINKY ENSURES THAT THE ENEMY CANNOT ADVANCE INTO THE STATION.

THEY HAVE TO GET THE ALIENS OUT SOMEHOW.

MISSION ACCOMPLISHED! BUT WHAT'S THAT SOUND?

UH-OH ... THEY'RE COMING BACK!

THIS SPACE STATION WON'T BE SAFE UNTIL THE TUNNEL IS DESTROYED.

HOLY FUZZBUTT!!!

THEY DID IT!

WHO KNEW THEY WOULD MAKE SUCH A GREAT TEAM?

ONCE AGAIN, THE SPACE STATION IS SAFE.

BINKY AND GRACIE INTEND TO KEEP IT THAT WAY.

CAPTAIN GRACIE SENDS
HER REPORT
TO F.U.R.S.T.
HEADQUARTERS.

BINKY NOT ONLY REMAINS A SPACE CAT ...

HE'S BEEN PROMOTED.

BINKY, SPACE CAT EXTRAORDINAIRE, IS BACK!!

GRACIE IS GETTING HER REWARD AS WELL.

SHE HAS BEEN ASSIGNED HER VERY OWN SPACE STATION TO PROTECT.

AND SHE'LL BE RIGHT NEXT DOOR!

BEFORE SHE LEAVES FOR HER NEW POSTING ...

rooop

BINKY GIVES HER A LITTLE SOMETHING ...

IN CASE SHE GETS LONELY.

prrrrrrrrrrr!

63